Cause and Effect
Reading Comprehension Book
Reading Level 3.5–5.0

Introduction

Welcome to the Edupress Cause and Effect Reading Comprehension Book. This resource is an effective tool for instruction, practice, and evaluation of student understanding. It includes ideas on how to introduce cause and effect to students, as well as activities to help teach and practice the concept.

The reproducible activities in this book are tailored to individual, small-group, and whole-class work. They include leveled reading passages, graphic organizers, worksheets, and detailed instruction pages. These activities provide opportunities to use text, illustrations, graphics, and combinations of these elements to identify cause-and-effect relationships.

The material in this book is written for readers at the 3.5–5.0 reading level. However, the activities can easily be adapted to your students' ability levels and your time frame. After introducing an activity to students, model it by working through one or two examples aloud. You may wish to also read text passages aloud to students, or they can be read silently or aloud by students. For students who need personalized help, individual and small-group activities have been included. These activities can be done alone or with a classroom aide for explicit instruction.

We know you will be pleased with the progress your students make in understanding cause and effect after using this book.

Edupress
12621 Western Avenue
Garden Grove, CA 92841
www.teachercreated.com

EP62363 • ©2010 Edupress
Reprinted, 2017
ISBN: 978-1-56472-153-2
Printed in U.S.A.

Table of Contents

Directions: Cause and Effect Match-Up

Whole Class ● ● ●

Introduce the idea of reading for cause and effect. Read a short picture book, such as *The Wind Blew* by Pat Hutchins. On a card or sentence strip, write, "The wind blew." Ask students what happens in the story when the wind blows. Then, on a card, write, "It took Mr. White's umbrella." Explain that the first sentence was the cause, and the second sentence was the effect. Then, ask what happens at the end of the story when the wind changes its mind.

Explain that the class will be matching Cause and Effect Cards. Display example cards: "I stayed out in the rain. I got wet."; "I dropped my pencil. I leaned over to pick it up." Remind students that the cause happens first, and the effect happens as a result of the cause. Divide the class into two teams. Reproduce a set of Cause and Effect Cards on page 4 for each team, and cut them apart. Review that a cause begins the process, and an event follows. Have one team read aloud a cause card. Students on both teams should search their Effect Cards for an appropriate match. The first team to find a correct match and read it aloud wins a point. Does the group agree it is a logical match? Repeat as time allows.

Individual ●

Reproduce several sets of Cause and Effect Cards and cut them apart. Give each student three or four pairs of cards that are mixed up. Ask students to match the pairs. Have them read their finished pairs aloud to you or provide them with an answer key to self-check.

Small Group ● ●

Divide the class into small groups. Reproduce the Cause and Effect Cards for each group, cut them apart, and mix them up. Lay the cards facedown on a desk. Explain the game of concentration. Students will take turns turning over two cards. If the students think the cards are a match, the student reads the pair aloud, and the group decides whether the pair is accurate. If the cards are correct, the student keeps them. Play continues to the left. Continue until one student has three matches and wins the game.

Answer Key

C The applesauce tasted bitter.
E Grandmother added sugar for sweetness.

C Glaciers show gradual melting. **E** Scientists are worried melting glaciers will harm animals' habitats.

C Cara wants to avoid eating too much junk food.
E She chooses fruits and vegetables for her snacks.

C The salamander is cold-blooded.
E It sits in the sunshine to get warm.

C The odor of the skunk was unpleasant.
E Amanda pinched her nose with her fingers.

C The cattle wandered away from the meadow.
E The farmer was concerned about finding them.

C Jack wants to be the best hockey player on the team.
E He practices daily to improve his skills.

C Prehistoric plants and animals died amd were buried.
E Fossils formed after millions of years of pressure.

C Maggie left her toys on the stairs.
E Her mother tripped on her way upstairs.

C I didn't put sunscreen on when I went outside.
E I got a terrible sunburn.

C Some insects have the colors and markings of plants in their habitats.
E This camouflage protects them from predators.

C Crystal felt the chill of the autumn wind.
E She was thankful that she had a sweater.

C Water droplets in clouds become very heavy.
E They fall to the ground as rain.

C Early settlers wanted to find land for homes and farms.
E They traveled west.

C The telephone rang.
E Jessica picked up the phone and said, "Hello?"

C Justin wanted to see what happened at the end of the novel.
E He asked his dad if he could stay up and read a little longer.

Cause and Effect Cards

C		E	
The applesauce tasted bitter.		Grandmother added sugar for sweetness.	
Glaciers show gradual melting.		Scientists are worried melting glaciers will harm animals' habitats.	
Cara wants to avoid eating too much junk food.		She chooses fruits and vegetables for her snacks.	
The salamander is cold-blooded.		It sits in the sunshine to get warm.	
The odor of the skunk was unpleasant.		Amanda pinched her nose with her fingers.	
The cattle wandered away from the meadow.		The farmer was concerned about finding them.	
Jack wants to be the best hockey player on the team.		He practices daily to improve his skills.	
Prehistoric plants and animals died and were buried.		Fossils formed after millions of years of pressure.	
Maggie left her toys on the stairs.		Her mother tripped on her way upstairs.	
I didn't put sunscreen on when I went outside.		I got a terrible sunburn.	
Some insects have the colors and markings of plants in their habitats.		This camouflage protects them from predators.	
Crystal felt the chill of the autumn wind.		She was thankful that she had a sweater.	
Water droplets in clouds become very heavy.		They fall to the ground as rain.	
Early settlers wanted to find land for homes and farms.		They traveled west.	
The telephone rang.		Jessica picked up the phone and said, "Hello?"	
Justin wanted to see what happened at the end of the novel.		He asked his dad if he could stay up and read a little longer.	

Directions: Historical Cause and Effect

Whole Class ●●●

Reproduce "A Land of Opportunities" or "An American Tradition" on page 6 or 7 and the graphic organizer on page 8 for each student as well as on transparencies. Have students volunteer to read paragraphs out loud. Then, ask students to find as many cause-and-effect pairings in the story as they can. Underline the cause and circle the corresponding effect on the transparency of the story. Then, complete the graphic organizer transparency as a class, writing the causes in the left column and the effects in the right column. Explain that asking, "Why did this happen?" and "What was the result?" can help determine cause and effect. Also explain that a cause can have more than one effect.

Individual ●

Reproduce "A Land of Opportunities" or "An American Tradition" and the graphic organizer for each student. Explain to students that they will read the passage and fill in the "Why" and "What" columns on the graphic organizer. Students who struggle with locating cause and effect will benefit from using this question strategy.

Small Group ●●

Divide students into pairs. Reproduce "A Land of Opportunities" or "An American Tradition" for both students, as well as one graphic organizer per pair. Explain that the pairs will read the passage together, taking turns reading the paragraphs out loud.

Then, using the graphic organizer, one student will fill in the cause (why) statements, and the other student will fill in the effect (what) statements. After completing the sheet, the students should check their answers to make sure they answer "Why?" and "What?" for each cause and effect.

Answer Key (suggested answers)

"A Land of Opportunities" (Page 6)

C: Immigrants seek the freedom America offers.
E: Immigrants come to America.

C: The United States has laws that say people have economic freedom. E: People are free to apply for any job. E: The money they earn from their jobs is theirs to spend.

C: Some governments have rules about free speech. E: The citizens are not allowed to write or speak their opinions. E: Their ideas must be the same as the government.

C: America has freedom of speech. E: People have the freedom to say or write what they think.

C: Some governments decide what religion its citizens will practice. E: People can get in trouble for worshipping a different way.

C: The United States is a land of religious freedom. E: People come to the United States to worship as they choose.

C: A U.S. citizen is 18 years old or older.
E: He or she can vote.

C: In some countries, citizens are not allowed to vote.
E: The government gets to make all the laws.

C: People are allowed to vote in America.
E: They can help change laws.

C: People hope to find better lives and have more choices.
E: They come to America.

"An American Tradition" (Page 7)

C: Parts of the United States were open range.
E: Horses and cattle roamed freely.

C: There were very few fences.
E: Ranch hands had to keep close watch on the cattle.

C: Ranchers needed to move cattle across the land.
E: They hired cowboys.

C: The Civil War ended. E: All the slaves were set free. E: Bazy became a free man.

C: Cowboys had to keep track of their herds.
E: The cattle were branded.

C: The cattle were branded.
E: Cowboys could identify their herds.

C: Bandits tried to steal cattle.
E: Cowboys had to defend their herds.

C: It took a long time to herd cattle.
E: Cowboys had to fight loneliness. E: Cowboys got sick.

C: Settlers wanted to keep animals out of their fields.
E: They built fences.

C: People settled in the Midwest.
E: Ranchers had to find other ways to get cattle to market.

C: The railroad expanded.
E: Ranchers could transport their cattle more easily.

C: Ranchers want to move their cattle quickly.
E: They use railroads and large trucks.

A Land of Opportunities

The United States has long been known as the Land of Opportunity. For many years, immigrants have come to America because they seek the freedom it offers.

The United States has laws that say its citizens have freedom. Because of these laws, people are free to apply for any job. No one else can tell them what job they must do. The money they earn from that job is theirs to spend or save as they desire. No one can tell them what to do with the money they earn.

Freedom of speech is another right that citizens in the United States have. Some governments have rules against free speech. Their citizens are not allowed to write or speak their opinions. Their ideas must be the same as those of the government. Because of the laws of the United States, people have the freedom to say what they think. They have the freedom to print their ideas in newspapers and in books. They might even write their ideas on the Internet. This is called freedom of speech.

The United States is a land of religious freedom. In some countries, the government decides the religion. This means that if a person wishes to worship in a different way, he or she could get in trouble. People are not able to worship as they please. Many people come to the United States so they can choose the way they will worship.

Voting is another right that people in the United States have. If a citizen is 18 years or older, he or she can vote. That is not true in every country. In some countries, only men can vote. Perhaps they must own some land. In many places, people are not allowed to vote at all! Because the citizens are not allowed to vote, the government gets to make all the laws. Even if the people don't like the laws that are made, they cannot change them. Because people are allowed to vote in America, they can play a part in changing laws they disagree with.

Hundreds of years ago, many people from other countries came to the United States. They were seeking freedom. They were looking for life, liberty, and the pursuit of happiness. That is now written in the Constitution. People still immigrate to America because of the same reasons. They hope to find a better life. They want to have choices. They hope to find freedoms that they did not have in their homelands. They come to find opportunities in the land we call the United States of America.

An American Tradition

Americans seem to love a good hamburger. They have been eating beef for hundreds of years. How does beef make it from the cattle ranch to become hamburgers and steaks?

Years ago, the western and southwestern parts of the United States were open range. Wild horses roamed freely on the land. However, cattle that belonged to ranchers roamed freely, too. There were very few fences. That meant ranch hands had to keep watch on the cattle. They made sure they were safe. It was their job to make sure the cattle stayed in one general area.

When it was time to send the cattle to market, the ranchers had another huge job. Ranchers needed to move cattle across the land. To do this, they hired cowboys. They spent months herding the cattle across the open land to get them to their destination. Working on a cattle drive was not easy.

Many cowboys were from Mexico. Others were former slaves. Hector Bazy was an African-American cowboy. Bazy was born a slave in Texas in 1851. When the Civil War ended, all the slaves were set free. Bazy became a free man. He worked as a cowboy and kept a journal on the life of a cowboy. His journal is housed at the Smithsonian Institute in Washington, D.C.

The hot, dirty work of a cowboy included long hours in the saddle. Cowboys had to keep track of their herds. The cattle were branded so the cowboys could identify the ones for which they were in charge. Often, bandits tried to steal these valuable animals. This meant cowboys had to defend their herd.

It took months to get from a cattle ranch in Texas to the railroads in Kansas and Missouri. This meant the cowboys had to fight the loneliness of being on the trail with only a few other workers. The long time in the field also caused many cowboys to get sick.

Then, things started to prevent them from using this method to get the cattle to market. Settlers moved west. They established their farms on the open plains. They plowed the land to grow crops to feed their families. They also built fences in order to keep their livestock on their land, because they wanted animals to stay out of their farm fields. The land that was once wide open, a perfect place for large groups of cattle to move across the land, was no longer open.

What was the result of the settlement of the Midwest? Ranchers had to find other ways to get their cattle to market. They took the cattle shorter distances to new railroad lines. In 1869, the transcontinental railroad joined the eastern and western United States. In the years that followed, the railroads continued to expand, covering more and more of the country. This allowed ranchers to transport their cattle more easily.

Being a rancher is still hard work. In order to move their cattle quickly, ranchers still use the railroad. They also use large trucks to get cattle to the railroads or to take them directly to market. It is a long road from the cattle ranch to the good old American hamburger!

Cause-and-Effect Graphic Organizer

Cause (Why did this happen?)　　　　　**Effect** (What was the result?)

Directions: "Ready to Go" Story

Individual/Small Group

Reproduce "Ready to Go" and "Ready to Go" Questions on pages 10 and 11 for each student. Have students read the story silently or aloud and answer the questions, then discuss their answers with a partner.

Whole Class

Reproduce the passage on a transparency and read it as a class. Divide the class into two teams. Have one player from each team come to the front of the room. Then, ask a question from the worksheet. The first player to answer correctly wins a point for his or her team. As an added challenge, ask students to identify other cause-and-effect examples in the story.

Answer Key

"Ready to Go" Questions (Page 11)

1. She didn't want to be bored on the long ride.
2. He wanted her to close the door so Jack wouldn't get out.
3. Jack will get out.
4. He wants their snacks.
5. He ate a kid's ice pop.
6. He is always thirsty.
7. He would eat too much.
8. He has a problem or question.

Ready to Go

Tasha looked around her bedroom one last time. Three hours would be a long time to be in the van. And she would be away from home for the whole weekend. She wanted to make sure she had enough to keep her busy while she was at her grandpa's house. Tasha picked two books, a drawing pad and colored pencils, and her music player. She put the items in her backpack and hurried downstairs.

Dad was packing the car. He had his hands full carrying the suitcases outside. "Tasha, please get the door," he said.

The Morissons always kept the door closed. If they didn't, their beagle, Jack, would run outside. Jack adored kids. He would always run across the street and into the backyard of the house where three little boys lived. Jack loved to play with the boys. Besides that, if Jack sat and looked at them with his pleading eyes, they would share whatever snack they might have.

One time, the youngest boy was standing with an ice pop in his hand. Jack didn't have to jump very far to snatch the ice pop. After that, Jack raced around and around the yard so that no one could catch him. The little boy was crying because he lost his ice pop. Everyone else was laughing very hard at Jack because his tan fur was purple from the icy treat.

Tasha didn't want to chase Jack today. As she was closing the door, he came running.

"You're too late, Jack!" Tasha laughed as she bent down to pet the determined dog. Jack looked at Tasha and wagged his tail.

"Okay, okay," Tasha said. Perhaps a toy would get Jack's mind off wanting to get out. She picked up a stuffed frog that made a squeaking sound. When Tasha tossed the toy to Jack, he grabbed it in his mouth and started to chew. The toy made a high-pitched squeak over and over again.

Soon Dad came back into the house. Sam, the boy who lived next door, was with him. Sam would take care of Jack while Tasha's family was out of town.

"Tasha, would you show Sam where everything is?" asked Dad.

"Okay, Dad," said Tasha. Then, she walked with Sam into the laundry room.

"Jack is always thirsty," Tasha explained. "So we keep his water bowl filled up."

"Got it," Sam was writing in a notebook so that he would remember everything.

"He likes to eat a little too much, so we only put dry food in his dish once in the morning and once at supper time. If we leave food in his dish all day, Jack will just eat and eat."

"Food only two times a day," repeated Sam.

"As soon as Jack finishes eating, we let him outside for a while. That is for obvious reasons," Tasha smiled.

Sam grinned and wrote the next step of instructions.

"Okay," Tasha continued talking as she and Sam walked back to the living room. "Do you have any questions?"

"I think I have all the important information. I will call your dad's cell phone if I have a problem."

"Thanks, Sam!" Tasha said. "I know Jack will be in good hands!"

"Ready to Go" Questions

Directions: Read the story "Ready to Go." Then, answer the questions.

★ 1 Why was Tasha bringing so many things with her?

★ 2 Why did Tasha's dad want her to close the door?

★ 3 What happens if the Morrisons leave the door open?

★ 4 Why does Jack look at the boys with pleading eyes?

★ 5 What event caused Jack's fur to become purple?

★ 6 Why does Jack always need a full water bowl?

★ 7 What would happen as a result of leaving Jack's food out all day?

★ 8 Why would Sam call Tasha's father?

Directions: Cause-and-Effect Signal Words

Individual ●

Reproduce Signal Words Fill-in-the-Blanks 1 and 2 on pages 13 and 14 for each student. Have the students fill in the blanks with the correct choices from the word bank. Explain that in some cases, more than one choice will fit in a blank. Remind students that it is important to reread each sentence with the selected choice to make sure the sentence makes sense.

Small Group ● ●

Divide students into pairs or small groups. Reproduce Signal Words Fill-in-the-Blanks 1 or 2 for each student in the group. Have the students work together to fill in the blanks with the correct choices. Then, have students discuss the answer for each sentence. Encourage students to read the complete sentence when giving their answer. Often, students are more aware of the appropriateness of their answer when they hear it in context. Next, ask the students to discuss and label the parts of each sentence (cause or effect).

Whole Class ● ● ●

Reproduce Signal Words Fill-in-the-Blanks 1 or 2 on a transparency. Write each of the words from the word banks on index cards, and place the cards in a bag or box. Divide the class into two teams. Explain that they will play a game locating the best sentence to fit each signal word. Have a student from each team come to the front and draw a card from the bag. The first person to say which sentence is a good fit for the word wins a point for his or her team. Continue with students from each team taking turns choosing a card.

Game tip: Some students will find it easier to have a copy of the transparency as a worksheet they can follow on their own desk. This may be the case for students with visual tracking difficulties or low vision.

As an alternative game, ask students to state a cause-and-effect sentence aloud using the words they drew.

Answer Key

Signal Words Fill-in-the-Blanks 1 (Page 13)

1. so
2. because/due to the fact that/since
3. due to the fact that/because/since
4. Consequently/As a result/Thus/Therefore
5. As a result/Consequently/Thus/Therefore
6. because/due to the fact that
7. The result/The outcome
8. The result/The outcome
9. Thus/so/therefore
10. because/since/due to the fact that

Signal Words Fill-in-the-Blanks 2 (Page 14)

1. The reason for
2. Consequently/As a result
3. so
4. because/due to the fact that
5. as a result/because
6. lead to
7. As a result/Consequently
8. because/due to the fact that
9. caused
10. The outcome

Signal Words Fill-in-the-Blanks 1

Name:_____

Directions: Choose the best word or words to finish each sentence. There can be more than one right answer.

1 Mrs. Anderson punched holes in the paper _____ she could put it in the notebook.

2 Darren wears a helmet when he plays football _____ _____ he wants to protect his head.

3 The parade was delayed _____ _____ it was raining cats and dogs.

4 The strong winds blew the bird nest to the ground. _____ the female bird built a new one.

5 The teams were tied. _____, fans were perched on the edge of their seats.

6 Dad took the car through the car wash _____ _____ mud was splattered all over it.

7 Andrew ran three miles every day for a month. _____ was that he placed first in the race.

8 Jesse wanted to sell the most candy bars. _____ would be winning a CD.

9 The little girl wanted to be just like her sister. _____, she walked around the house wearing her shoes.

10 Mary took a shovel in her car _____ _____ snow was in the forecast.

WORD BANK

thus

due to the fact that

as a result
since

therefore

so

consequently

the result

because

the outcome

Signal Words Fill-in-the-Blanks 2

Directions: Choose the best word or words to finish each sentence. There can be more than one right answer.

1 _____ the bird's quick flight was the sound of the approaching dog.

2 The bicycle hit a pothole. _____, the biker fell to the pavement.

3 I opened my mouth wide _____ the dentist could examine my teeth.

4 The obedient pooch sat still _____ he wanted a treat.

5 Several trees were blown over _____ of the violent winds.

6 Fear of catching the flu _____ the students washing their hands frequently.

7 Abbey had concentrated on her chess moves. _____, she was winning the match.

8 Sheila flossed her teeth several times a day _____ she did not want any cavities.

9 The freezing temperatures _____ the cement sidewalk to contract.

10 _____ of all the rain was a large harvest.

WORD BANK

the reason for

due to the fact that

as a result

effect

lead to

so

consequently

because

caused

the outcome

Individual

Reproduce "The Amusement Park" on page 16 or "A Miniature World" on page 17, along with the graphic organizer on page 18, for each student. Explain that students will read the story and then write sentences or draw pictures in the graphic organizer for the cause-and-effect examples they identify in the text. If students need additional space, instruct them to continue on the back of the graphic organizer.

Small Group

Divide the class into pairs. Reproduce "The Amusement Park" or "A Miniature World" for each student, as well as a graphic organizer for each pair.

Have the students take turns reading the story aloud. Then, have the students take turns identifying examples of cause and effect in the text. For example, if the first student finds an example of a cause, he or she should write or draw a picture that represents it in the graphic organizer. Then, the other student will write or draw the related effect. The activity continues until the graphic organizer is filled.

Whole Class

Reproduce a copy of "The Amusement Park" or "A Miniature World" for each student. Also, reproduce the graphic organizer on a transparency.

Have the students read the passage aloud with a partner. Then, split the students into two groups. One student will come to the overhead and write or draw either a cause or an effect from the text. Then, have a student from the other group write or draw the corresponding cause or effect. Continue in this manner until the graphic organizer is filled. Repeat with the second story. Then, discuss the activity as a class.

Answer Key (suggested answers)

"The Amusement Park" (Page 16)

Cause: Ming was excited about her field trip.
Effect: She woke up early.

Cause: Ming didn't want to get a sunburn.
Effect: She put on sunscreen.

Cause: Ming and others got good grades.
Effect: School rewarded them with free tickets to the park.

Cause: Ming brought a book to read.
Effect: She wouldn't get bored on the bus.

Cause: Ming was nervous about riding the coasters.
Effect: Her friend Ben told her not to worry.

Cause: Mrs. Osborne didn't want anyone to get lost in the park.
Effect: She made sure everyone had a buddy.

Cause: The Wagon Wheel made the girls dizzy.
Effect: They lost their balance.

Cause: The Screamer was the best ride Ming had been on.
Effect: She rode it three more times.

Cause: Everyone was excited.
Effect: They talked all at once.

Cause: Mrs. Osborne shushed the group.
Effect: They could hear her.

Cause: Mrs. Osborne would buy them lunch.
Effect: The kids cheered.

Cause: The kids ate a lot.
Effect: They felt like they were going to explode.

Cause: Ming made three baskets.
Effect: She won a huge teddy bear.

Cause: She had too many prizes.
Effect: Her friends helped her carry them.

Cause: The kids were tired.
Effect: They slept the whole way home.

"A Miniature World" (Page 17)

Cause: Justin needed an empty jar for his science projects.
Effect: He emptied the Curly Crunchers jar.

Cause: He needed to get the jar ready for his project.
Effect: He washed and dried it.

Cause: Justin's class wanted to show how the water cycle worked.
Effect: They were making terrariums.

Cause: The kids would observe the terrariums.
Effect: They would understand the water cycle and write reports.

Cause: Kids follow directions.
Effect: Their projects will work.

Cause: Too much water would gather at the top of the terrarium.
Effect: The water would fall.

Cause: Too much water collects in clouds. Effect: It rains.

Cause: Justin couldn't wait to see how the water cycle worked.
Effect: He smiled.

Cause: Justin turned the jar into a miniature world.
Effect: His parents would be proud.

The Amusement Park

Ming woke up early because she was so excited about her field trip. She ran through the house getting ready. On her way out the door, she put on lots of sunscreen. She knew being in the sun all day could cause a bad sunburn. She didn't want anything to ruin her day!

Today Ming was going to the amusement park. Along with her classmates, she had worked hard to get good grades all year. As a result, the school was rewarding them with free tickets to the park. Ming ran the three blocks to the school where a bus was waiting. As they boarded the bus, Mrs. Osborne reminded the kids that it would take an hour to get there. Ming was glad she had brought a book to read so she wouldn't get bored on the long ride.

When the bus pulled up to the park, Ming looked at the tall roller coasters. She got a little nervous imagining what it would be like to fly through the air on a roller coaster. "Don't worry, Ming," her friend Ben said when he saw the look on her face. "You're going to love it!"

When they entered the big park, Mrs. Osborne made sure everyone had a buddy so no one would get lost. They made a plan to meet for lunch, and the group took off toward the rides.

Ming and her buddy Karla headed toward the Wagon Wheel, a ride that twirled the girls around. When they got off, the girls were both dizzy and laughing. The spinning ride made them lose their balance as they tried to walk.

They finally made their way to one of the large roller coasters: The Screamer. After their first ride on The Screamer, Ming was hooked. She decided it was the best ride she had ever been on and rode it three more times before lunch.

The girls met the rest of their group at lunch time. Everyone was so excited that they were all talking at once. Mrs. Osborne shushed the group so they could hear her. She told them she was going to buy them lunch as another reward. The hungry kids cheered. Ming and the others ate so much they felt like they were going to explode. They decided to play some games to work off their big lunch.

Ming started with the basketball hoops. She made three baskets in a row and won a huge teddy bear. Then, she tried bowling and pinball. Soon she had so many prizes she couldn't carry them all. Her friends had to help her. As they walked back to the bus, they all agreed it had been a great day. After they got on the bus, the kids were so tired that they slept the whole way home.

A Miniature World

Justin emptied the last of the Curly Crunchers into a plastic bag. He needed an empty jar for his science project. The Curly Crunchers jar was perfect. He washed and dried the jar so it would be ready for his project the next day.

Justin's class was making terrariums to show how the water cycle worked. The terrariums would be like tiny worlds. After they observed them, the kids would understand how the water cycle worked. Then, they could write their reports.

Mrs. Gomez had told the class they had to make sure they followed the directions for making the terrariums. If they didn't, their projects wouldn't work. First, they had to put a layer of soil in the bottom of the jar. Then, they would plant small plants in the dirt. This would

be a small version of the plants that grow on Earth. Next, they would sprinkle water on their plants like rain. Later, the water would evaporate, or rise to the top of the jar. When too much water gathered at the top, it would fall. This would be like when clouds collect too many water droplets. Mrs. Gomez called this condensation. She explained that when the clouds can't hold anymore water, it rains. Then, the cycle starts all over again.

Justin looked at his empty jar and smiled. He couldn't wait to fill it with dirt and plants to see how the water cycle worked. His parents were going to be so proud when they saw how he turned the Curly Crunchers jar into a miniature world!

Cause-and-Effect Graphic Organizer

Name:_____

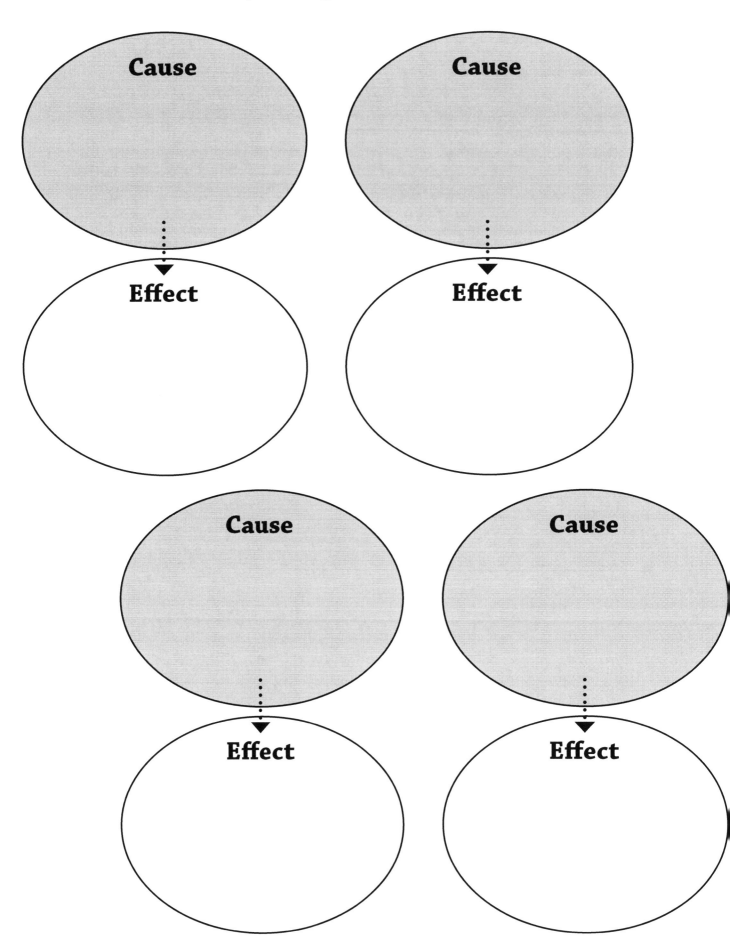

Directions: Picture Match-Up

Individual

Reproduce multiple sets of the Picture Pair Cards on pages 20–23. Give several sets of cards to each student. Younger students or those who struggle with the concept of cause and effect might start with three or four pairs of cards. Other students might use 10 pairs.

Model matching the corresponding cause-and-effect pairs; then, have students try on their own. For an additional challenge, have students write a sentence for each picture pair.

Small Group

Divide the class into pairs. Reproduce a complete set of Picture Pair Cards for each pair of students. Explain that they will play a memory match-up game. Spread the cards facedown on a table and have students take turns turning two cards over. If the cards are not a match, they must turn them facedown again. When a student gets a matching pair, he or she must identify the cause and the effect in order to keep the cards. The first student to get three matches wins the game.

Whole Group

Reproduce two complete sets of Picture Pair Cards. Use two bags to separate the card sets. Then divide the class into two teams. Give each team a bag. Explain that the first team to match all of the cards correctly wins! Check to make sure students have matched picture pairs correctly.

For an additional challenge, have the students write a sentence for each picture pair. If some students are struggling with writing cause-and-effect sentences, review possible signal or connecting words (so, because, since, as a result, the reason that, consequently, therefore, nevertheless, thus, due to the fact, the outcome was), and write them on the board for student reference as they are writing.

Picture Pair Cards 2

Picture Pair Cards 3

EP62363 Cause and Effect, RL 3.5–5.0 ©Edupress

Picture Pair Cards 4

Directions: Cause and Effect Picture Clues

Individual/Small Group

Reproduce Missing Cause and Effect 1 or 2 on page 25 or 26 for each student. Explain that they will examine each picture and write what the corresponding cause or effect would be.

Whole Class ● ● ●

Reproduce the pictures from Missing Cause and Effect 1 and 2 on card stock or construction paper. Then, place the cards facedown on a table in the front of the room. Divide the class into two teams. Have one person from each team come to the front and choose a card. The students should not look at the card until you say, "Go." Then, each student writes a cause-and-effect sentence on the board based on the picture clue on the card. The first person to write a complete, accurate sentence wins a point for his or her team. Continue the game in this fashion as time allows or until a predetermined score has been reached.

Students who struggle with written language may need to give their sentence orally. You may also score the students simply on their ability to state the corresponding cause or effect.

Answer Key (suggested answers)

Missing Cause and Effect 1 (Page 25)

1. Effect: The crowd claps.
   Cause: The crowd watched a dance or theater performance.

2. Effect: The man has to pump gas into his car.
   Cause: The car ran out of gas.

3. Effect: The man takes his temperature.
   Cause: He feels like he might have a fever.

4. Cause: The roller coaster goes over the hill.
   Effect: The kids scream as they go down the hill.

5. Cause: Someone holds a match to sticks.
   Effect: The sticks burn.

6. Cause: The woman fills the pool.
   Effect: The kids can go swimming.

Missing Cause and Effect 2 (Page 26)

1. Effect: The boy has to chase the dog.
   Cause: The dog pulled hard on the leash.

2. Effect: The boy's bicycle gets a flat tire.
   Cause: The boy rode over something sharp.

3. Effect: The ball goes through the hoop.
   Cause: Someone shot a basket.

4. Cause: Someone pushes the button on the blender full of fruit.
   Effect: The blender makes a smoothie.

5. Cause: A girl spots an ice cream truck.
   Effect: She buys an ice cream cone.

6. Cause: A person pushes the door button.
   Effect: The door opens and the person goes through.

Missing Cause and Effect 1

Name:_____

Directions: Look at each picture. Write the missing cause or effect. For example, look at the kids on the roller coaster. What do you think will happen when they go over the hill?

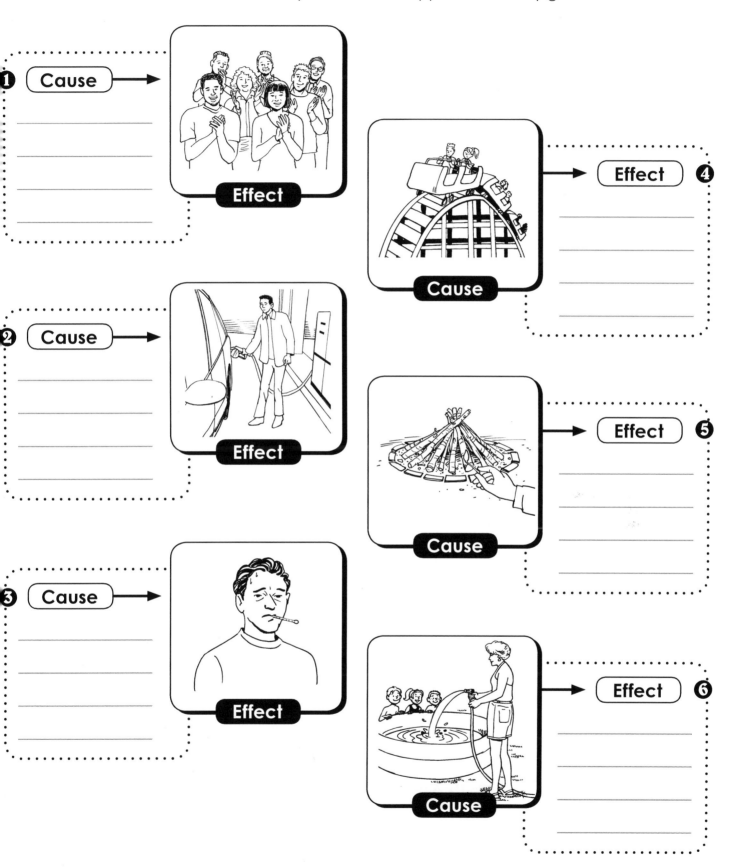

1 (Cause) → Effect

_____
_____
_____
_____

4 Effect ← Cause

_____
_____
_____

2 (Cause) → Effect

_____
_____
_____
_____

5 Effect ← Cause

_____
_____
_____

3 (Cause) → Effect

_____
_____
_____
_____

6 Effect ← Cause

_____
_____
_____

Missing Cause and Effect 2

Name:_____

Directions: Look at each picture. Write the missing cause or effect. For example, look at the boy on the bicycle. Why do you think the bike has a flat tire?

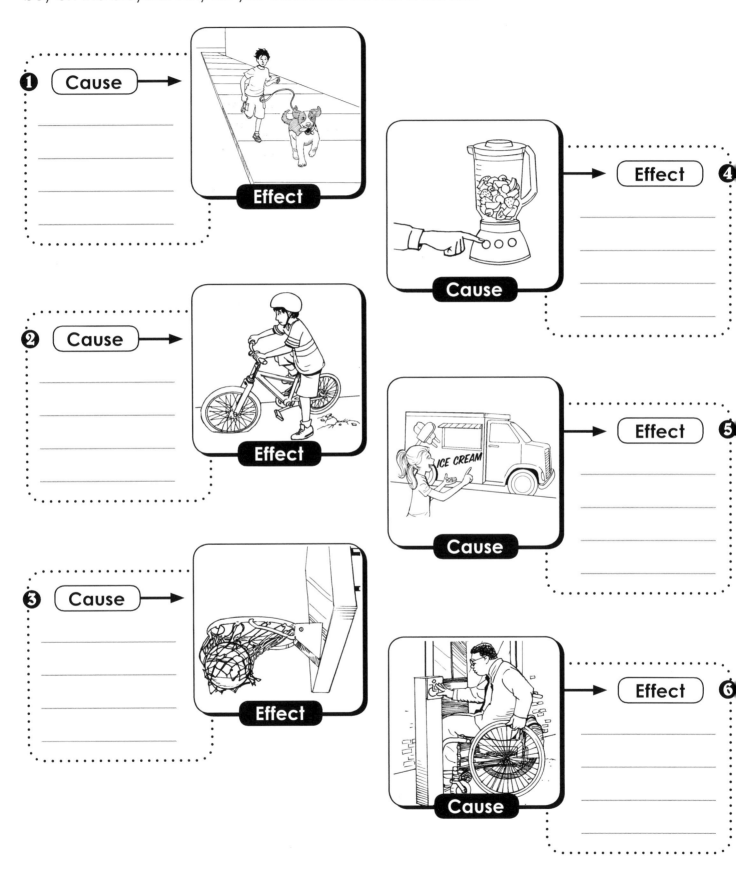

① Cause ➤

Effect

② Cause ➤

Effect

③ Cause ➤

Effect

Effect **④**

Cause

Effect **⑤**

Cause

Effect **⑥**

Cause

Directions: Missing Cause or Effect

Individual

Reproduce Finish the Sentence 1 and 2 on pages 28 and 29 for each student. Explain that either the cause or the effect is provided. Tell students to fill in the blanks with the missing parts. Encourage them to read their complete sentences to make sure they have created logical sentences. Score based on sentence completeness and ability to understand the meaning.

Small Group ● ●

Pair students with partners, and give a different Finish the Sentence sheet to each student. Explain that this is a "think quick" activity. One student will read each sentence part on the first worksheet, and the other partner will finish the sentence. The "reader" will record the partner's answers. Then, have students switch roles with the new reader reading and filling in the second worksheet.

Whole Class ● ● ●

Reproduce one of the Finish the Sentence worksheets on a transparency. Divide the class into two teams, and have one person from each team play each round. Show one sentence at a time on the overhead. The first person to yell out a needed cause or effect wins a team point. Silly sentences are encouraged!

Answer Key (suggested answers)

Finish the Sentence 1 (Page 28)

1. I was very hungry
2. he could see to drive
3. The boy felt sick
4. he fell off
5. it was being petted
6. the temperature was so high
7. they ate all the snacks
8. the player broke a rule

Finish the Sentence 2 (Page 29)

1. it can easily blend in with the snow
2. we were very late for dinner
3. we won our first game
4. it is too hot to drink
5. The plant grew very big
6. I got a bad grade on my test
7. I packed up my books and went to the library
8. I got a rash all over my ankles

Finish the Sentence 1

Name:_____

Directions: Read the sentences. Write a cause or an effect to finish each sentence.

 1 I ate everything on my plate because _____

_____.

 2 My father scraped the ice from the windshield so _____

_____.

 3 _____. Therefore, he decided to
stay home.

 4 Clayton tried to ride his skateboard across the rough rocks.
Consequently, _____

_____.

 5 The kitten began to purr because _____

_____.

 6 Sam was sweating due to the fact that _____

_____.

 7 The football team was starving. Therefore, _____

_____.

 8 The referee blew his whistle because _____

_____.

Finish the Sentence 2

Name:_____

Directions: Read the sentences. Write a cause or an effect to finish each sentence.

 1 The rabbit's fur turns white in the winter so that _____

_____ .

 2 We got lost while driving to the restaurant. Therefore, _____

_____ .

 3 Our coach required us to practice three times weekly. As a result, _____

_____ .

 4 Grandmother puts ice cubes in her coffee because _____

_____ .

 5 _____ because it

got plenty of sunshine and water.

 6 The reason I had a bad day was _____

_____ .

 7 I couldn't read with all the noise, so _____

_____ .

 8 I stepped in some poison ivy, and _____

_____ .

Directions: Using Graphic Organizers

Individual ●

Reproduce the Water Jug and Sports Goal Graphic Organizers on pages 31 and 32 for each student. Review each graphic organizer with the students, explaining that *because* the water is being poured from the bottle, the glass is filling up; and *because* the ball is going into the net, the team will score a point. Using a book they've recently read, have the students fill in causes with related effects. Help them make the "pouring = full glass" or "goal = points" connection with cause-and-effect relationships from their book. To help them find causes and effects, ask them why a character did something, or point to a picture and ask how an object got where it is. For extra space, use the additional lines provided on the organizer. Students who have difficulty with writing might draw pictures to complete the graphic organizer.

Whole Class ●●●

Reproduce the Water Jug or Sports Goal Graphic Organizer on a transparency. Explain that the class will use the graphic organizer to plan a story. Then, students will work together to create the story.

As a class, choose a topic for the story, such as "pets." Ask volunteers to give ideas to fill in the details of the graphic organizer. For example, Cause: Dogs need exercise. Effect: Therefore, they need to be walked. Repeat with more causes and effects. Use the extra lines to record the cause-and-effect examples the class comes up with.

Then, brainstorm to create a beginning sentence, or main idea, for the story. Write it on the board or a transparency. Then, have students take turns adding sentences to the story, including the cause-and-effect ideas the class came up with.

After the story is complete, have the group analyze it for cause-and-effect sentences. Use a blue marker to underline causes that were included in the story. Use a red marker to underline effects.

Alternate idea: Brainstorm for a topic and beginning sentence. Then, split the class into two groups. Have each group create a story. Then, as a class, evaluate the stories for cause-and-effect relationships. Compare stories: How are they similar? How are they different?

Note: These activities work best if the students are writing on a lined transparency so that everyone will be able to see the story that is being discussed.

Water Jug Graphic Organizer

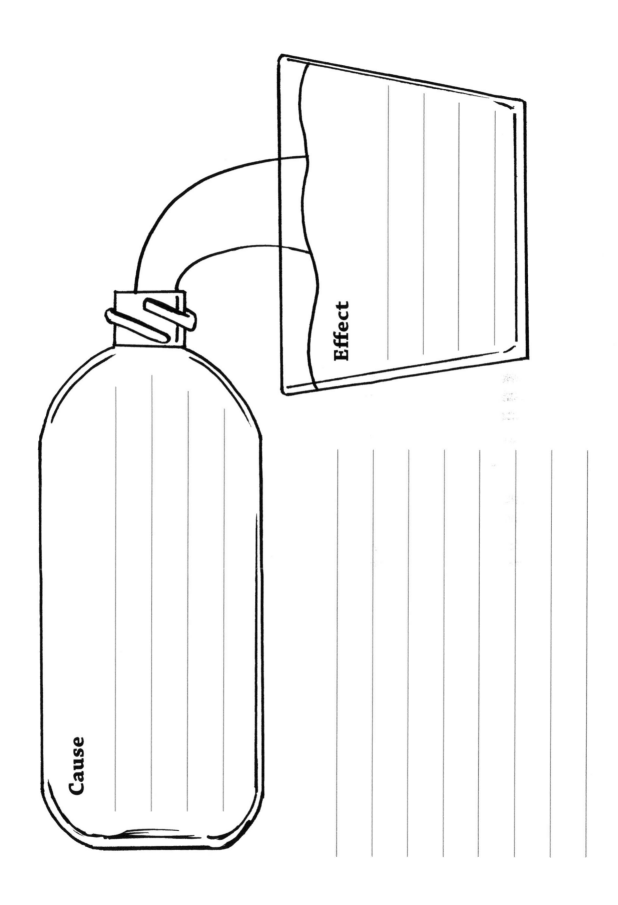

Cause

Effect

Sports Goal Graphic Organizer

Effect

Cause

Directions: Using Signal Words

Individual

Reproduce "The Clever Monkey" on page 34 and Putting "The Clever Monkey" In Order on page 35 for each student. Explain that "The Clever Monkey" sentences are mixed up, and that they will be putting them in order. First students will add cause-and-effect signal words from the word bank to each sentence or pair of sentences to make them into a cause-and-effect relationship. Remind students that signal words are words that let you know you're reading about a cause and effect. Review the words in the word bank together. Explain that more than one answer is possible. Then, have students write the sentences in the right order to create a story on the Putting "The Clever Monkey" In Order worksheet.

Small Group

Divide students into small groups. Reproduce Putting "The Clever Monkey" in Order for each group. Using the sentences from the Individual activity, have students work together to put the sentences in order.

For further practice with signal words, reproduce the list of signal words on page 34 on a transparency and display for the students. Have them write a fill-in-the-blank sentence (with the signal word missing) for each. Then, have partners exchange sentences and fill in the missing words. Each student should also mark the cause (C) and effect (E) component of each sentence. Partners can compare and discuss their answers when they are finished.

Whole Class

Reproduce the list of signal words on page 34 on a transparency and display for the students. Have each student write three sentences using the signal words. Divide the class into two teams. Have students from each team take turns reading one of their sentences. Is the sentence written correctly? If the other team can correctly identify the cause and the effect, that team wins a point. Play continues with teams alternating turns.

Answer Key

"The Clever Monkey"
suggested answers (Page 34)

1. so
2. because
3. As a result
4. Finally
5. For this reason
6. because
7. Then

Putting "The Clever Monkey" in Order
(Page 35)

The family of monkeys had been taking a nap because they were tired from playing all day. But, one monkey was very hungry. For this reason, he couldn't sleep. He wanted to find some food so his stomach would stop growling. He spotted a bunch of bananas, but he couldn't reach them because they were too high. Finally, he found a long branch he could use to knock them down. He took a mighty swing at the plant. As a result, the bananas rained down on him. Then, the rest of the monkeys came running when they saw the feast the clever monkey had found.

The Clever Monkey

Name:_____

Directions: Use the words in the word bank to make the sentences into cause-and-effect sentences. Write the words in the blanks. Words can be used more than once.

1. He wanted to find some food _____ his stomach would stop growling.

2. The family of monkeys had been taking a nap _____ they were tired from playing all day.

3. He took a mighty swing at the plant. _____ , the bananas rained down on him.

4. _____ , he found a long branch he could use to knock them down.

5. But, one monkey was very hungry. _____ , he couldn't sleep.

6. He spotted a bunch of bananas, but he couldn't reach them _____ they were too high.

7. _____ , the rest of the monkeys came running when they saw the feast the clever monkey had found.

Word Bank

Then	Finally
because	As a result
For this reason	so

Putting "The Clever Monkey" in Order

Name: _____

Directions: Use the cause-and-effect sentences you wrote to put the story in order.
Think about what might have happened first, second, third, etc.

The Clever Monkey

_____

_____

_____

_____

_____

_____

_____

_____

_____

_____

_____

_____

_____

_____

_____

_____

Individual ●

Reproduce "Leaf It to Us" and the "Leaf It to Us" Recording Sheet on pages 37 and 38. Explain that the students should read the story for understanding, watching for examples of cause and effect. Then, students should use the recording page to list the cause-and-effect ideas present in the story.

Small Group ●●

Divide the class into small groups. Reproduce "Leaf It to Us" and the corresponding recording sheet for each group. Have the small groups read the story together, taking turns reading aloud. Then, as a group, they should record the cause-and-effect examples from the story on the sheet. Finally, have each group share and discuss their findings with the class. Compare different groups' findings.

Whole Class ●●●

Reproduce "Leaf It to Us" on a transparency. Also, reproduce one recording sheet for each student. Tell students they should listen for cause-and-effect examples. Read the story aloud. After the entire story has been read, remove the transparency, and give the students one minute to record as many cause-and-effect pairings from the story as they can remember. Students will share answers with the class and discuss accuracy. The student with the most accurate answers wins a classroom reward (free time, extra recess, silent reading, a beanbag chair to use for the day, etc.).

Answer Key (suggested answers)

"Leaf It to Us" Recording Sheet (Page 38)

Cause: Grandparents fiftieth wedding anniversary. Effect: The family is having a huge dinner. Effect: Everyone would be there.

Cause: They had very little money. Effect: They had no gift.

Cause: Parents can't afford to give kids a loan. Effect: They decide to make a gift instead.

Cause: Madison and Frank wanted to look for a present. Effect: They walked downtown.

Cause: Madison wanted to look more. Effect: They went to the next store.

Cause: The grandparents like gifts the kids make.
Effect: They decide to make a homemade picture frame.

Cause: They did not have enough money for the frame.
Effect: They had to figure out how to make enough money to pay for the kit.

Cause: They saw all the leaves on the ground. Effect: They got an idea to have a leaf-raking business.

Cause: They left flyers at the store. Effect: People saw them and began to call them to rake leaves.

Cause: They worked hard. Effect: People started telling their friends about "Leaf It to Us."

Cause: They saved part of the money from their jobs. Effect: They could buy a frame kit.

Cause: They wrapped their gift. Effect: Their grandparents could not tell what the present was.

Cause: Their grandparents will have many pictures from the dinner. Effect: They will need a frame.

Cause: The kids made the gift. Effect: The grandparents liked it.

Leaf It to Us

Madison and Frank had a problem. Soon it would be their grandparents' fiftieth wedding anniversary. Their family was throwing a huge family dinner to celebrate it. Everyone would be there. Their cousins from New York, New Mexico, and Arkansas were coming. Everyone would have a special gift—everyone except Madison and Frank. They had no gift, because they had very little money.

"Maybe we could ask Mom and Dad for a loan," said Madison.

"They are already spending a lot of money on the dinner," said Frank. "They can't afford it. Maybe we could make them a gift instead."

"Maybe," said Madison. "Or maybe we can find something nice on sale."

That afternoon, Madison and Frank walked downtown. They wanted to look around for the perfect gift idea for the anniversary. First, they went to the craft store. They saw a kit for making a picture frame.

"That looks like a good idea," said Frank. "They will have lots of pictures from the anniversary dinner."

"I want to look a little more before we decide," said Madison.

Frank and Madison walked to the next store. Inside they saw pretty vases and beautiful coffee mugs.

"They have a flower garden. A vase is a good idea. They also like to drink coffee," said Madison.

"I think they would like the picture frame best because they like gifts we make." Frank announced after they were finished looking.

When they went back to the store with the frame kit, they looked at the price. They did not have enough money. Frank and Madison knew they would have to figure out how to earn enough to pay for the kit.

As they walked home, they shuffled their feet through the leaves. Seeing all the leaves on the ground gave them an idea. They could start a business raking leaves!

That afternoon Frank and Madison made flyers. They called their business "Leaf It to Us." They put some of the flyers at the store so people would see them when they paid for their things.

Soon people began to call Madison and Frank to rake the leaves in their yards. The two yard rakers worked very hard, and people started telling their friends about "Leaf It to Us."

Every time Madison and Frank had a leaf raking job, they saved part of the money so that they could buy the frame kit.

Finally, Frank and Madison had enough money saved, and they bought the kit. They were so excited! The frame would be a perfect gift for the anniversary celebration!

They assembled and decorated the frame. Then, they wrapped it so that Grandmother and Grandfather could not tell what it was.

Soon, the big day came. Madison and Frank waited for their grandparents to get to their gift. They were so happy to get the frame.

"We will need a frame because we'll have so many great pictures from this dinner," said Grandfather.

"I like it, too, because you made it," said Grandmother.

As Madison and Frank walked over to the cake table, they were talking about what a hit the present was.

"Leaf it to us!" they both said at the same time.

"Leaf It to Us" Recording Sheet

Name:_____

Directions: Read "Leaf It to Us." Then, write examples of cause and effect from the story on the lines below.

• Cause •	• Effect •

Directions: Cause and Effect Story Starters

Whole Class

Introduce the activity by reading a book that exemplifies cause and effect, such as one of Laura Joffe Numeroff's books, including *If You Give a Mouse a Cookie*, *If You Give a Moose a Muffin*, or *If You Give a Pig a Pancake*. Discuss the examples of cause and effect throughout the story.

Individual/Small Group

Reproduce Cause-and-Effect Stories on page 40 for each student. Have each student choose an idea from the list. Students should write their own cause-and-effect stories in the style of the story read as a class. This is a time for students to generalize their understanding of cause and effect into their own writing. The stories they write may be silly or serious. Then, have students work in pairs. They should share their stories with each other, labeling all of the cause-and-effect examples they can find. Then, invite volunteers to share their stories with the rest of the class.

Check to make sure students have included examples of cause and effect in their stories. Monitor partner work to make sure they are correctly identifying cause-and-effect pairs. At the end of the activity, put all of the stories in a binder to create a class book.

Cause-and-Effect Stories

Name:_____

Directions: Think about the cause-and-effect story that you read with your class. Then, choose one of the story starters below, or think of your own. Write your story on the lines. Draw one example of cause and effect from your story in the boxes below.

- If you give me a bicycle . . .
- If you give a frog a trampoline . . .
- If you give my class a pizza . . .
- If you give my teacher a farm . . .
- If you give my mom a chicken . . .
- If you give me a treehouse . . .

_____

_____

_____

_____

_____

_____

_____

_____

_____

_____

Cause	**Effect**

Directions: Cause and Effect with Science

Individual ●

Reproduce either "Animal Camouflage" or "Waiting for Spring" and their corresponding question sheets on pages 42–45 for each student. Explain that each student should read the passage, paying special attention to cause-and-effect relationships, then answer the questions. You may also wish to have the students mark each cause and effect by underlining the cause and circling the effect, or drawing an arrow from the cause to the effect. When all students have finished, go over the worksheets as a class.

Small Group/Whole Class ●●/●●●

Complete the passage and question activity for individuals. Then, split the class into groups of three or four students. Have the students brainstorm other cause-and-effect examples from nature. Allow the groups time to research on the Internet or use other resource materials. Provide each group with materials to create a poster illustrating one cause-and-effect relationship they learned about. Have each group present their poster to the class.

Answer Key

"Animal Camouflage" Questions (Page 43)

1. They need to hide from other animals that want to eat them.
2. They are white to blend in with the snow so predators can't find them.
3. Their bellies are white so that they can't be seen by animals from below.
4. They can't tell the difference between zebras and grass.
5. It makes them look like a bigger animal.

"Waiting for Spring" Questions (Page 45)

1. There is not much food available in winter.
2. Turtles bury themselves in mud to stay warm and hide from enemies.
3. They live off their stored body fat.
4. They want to make the walls thick for winter.
5. They hibernate to stay cool.

Animal Camouflage

Many animals eat other animals in order to survive. That means animals need a way to hide from bigger animals. They also hide from the animals they are hunting. This is because an animal has less time to run away when it is attacked if it doesn't see its predator. If an animal is able to surprise another creature, it can get a tasty meal.

Camouflage is one way animals are able to hide. Camouflage means blending in with the environment by having a certain color, pattern, or shape that allows an animal to hide.

Many animals and insects have the same coloring as their habitat. At first look, a predator may not be able to see them. Thus, they are safe from harm. Many arctic animals use color camouflage. They are white like their snowy environment. This makes it hard for predators to find them. Creatures in other habitats have coloring camouflage as well. Sharks have light-colored bellies, so other creatures cannot see them from below. The top of their bodies are dark so they can't be seen when looking down into the dark ocean. Even insects use color camouflage. Many insects are green to blend in with plant life. They can also be brown so they blend in with tree trunks and branches.

Camouflage is not limited to color. Skin and fur patterns can be the same as the animals' habitat. A zebra's stripes are a good example. They help it blend in with the tall, swaying grasses where it lives. The lion is a predator of the zebra. Because lions are color blind, it is hard for them to tell the difference between the grass and the zebra. The zebra also blends in with other zebras when they are gathered together. Because they all have the same pattern, the lion thinks it is looking at one large animal.

Some creatures also have the shape of things in their habitat. One example is the walking stick. You may have seen a walking stick before and not even known it! This is due to the fact that the walking stick's brown-gray color is the same as nearby twigs. It looks exactly like a stick on the ground. Therefore, you could probably only tell it was an insect if it moved.

Animals can even use camouflage to look like another animal. This kind of camouflage is called mimicry. Moths are good examples. The markings on some moth wings look like giant eyes. As a result, animals think the moth is a much bigger creature than it actually is. Because of this, predators will leave the moth alone.

The world of camouflage is fascinating. Colors, patterns, and shapes all play a part. What would you do to hide in *your* environment?

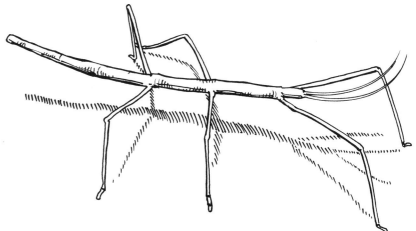

"Animal Camouflage" Questions

Name:_____

★1 **Why do animals need a way to hide?**

_____
_____
_____
_____

★2 **Why are many arctic animals white?**

_____
_____
_____
_____

★3 **Why do sharks have light-colored bellies?**

_____
_____

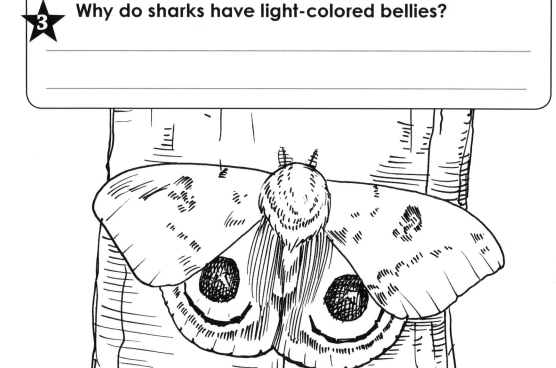

★4 **What is a result of lions being color-blind?**

_____
_____
_____
_____

★5 **How does mimicry help some moths?**

_____
_____
_____
_____

Waiting for Spring

Spring, summer, and fall are seasons when most animals are active. Winter can be very different. It is hard to find food in the winter. Therefore, many animals hibernate. Hibernation means the animals become inactive. Because they don't use a lot of energy, they don't need a lot of food.

Some examples of animals that hibernate are bears, bats, fish, and chipmunks. Squirrels, skunks, opossums, and frogs can hibernate, too. Even some insects, such as hornets, hibernate.

During hibernation, the animal's body needs to slow down. In order to save energy, the animal's heart rate and breathing slow down. The body temperature of the animal also drops.

But animals do need a little energy, even when hibernating. In order to survive, bears use their stored body fat. The animals eat a lot in the fall to build up their bodies. This helps them survive until spring. Then, there will be much more food to eat.

Some animals that live in the water also hibernate. Some types of turtles bury themselves in the mud at the bottom of ponds. Because the turtle's body slows down so much, it can live off the small amounts of oxygen in the mud. It actually stops breathing through its lungs. Turtles have special skin cells in their tails. The oxygen they need sinks in through these cells. Turtles can live like this for two or three months. This helps them get through the coldest winter weather. Burying themselves in the mud also keeps them safe from enemies.

Some insects need to hibernate, too. One example is hornets. Hornets live in paper-like nests. All summer, the hornets add to the walls of the nest. By the time winter arrives, the walls of the nest are thick. Many of the hornets die off in the fall. But the ones that stay are kept warm by the thick walls of the nest until spring. When warm weather hits, they become active again.

Hibernation does not always happen in the winter. Sometimes animals hibernate in the summer because the weather is too hot. Some desert animals wait out the heat by burying themselves in the sand or in burrows. This keeps them cooler.

Whether in winter or summer, animals hibernate for survival. It is a way their bodies have adapted to their environments. Because of this adaptation, they manage to survive to become active again when the harsh weather is over.

"Waiting for Spring" Questions

Name:_____

 1 What is one reason animals hibernate?

_____
_____
_____

 2 Why do turtles bury themselves in mud?

_____
_____
_____

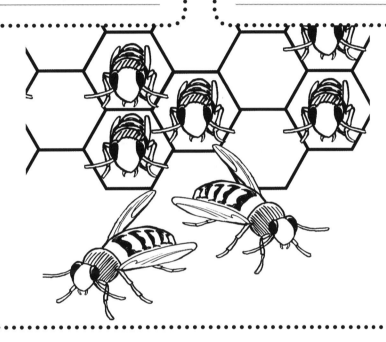

3 How do bears get energy during the winter months?

_____
_____

 4 Why do hornets add to their paper nests?

_____
_____
_____

5 Why do animals hibernate during hot weather?

_____
_____
_____

Directions: Think Quick! Games

Small Group ● ●

Play a game with Think Quick! Cards 1 and 2 on pages 47 and 48. Reproduce a set of cards for each group of four students. Place the cards facedown in the middle of the group. Students take turns drawing a card and reading it to the group. The first person to come up with an ending for the sentence wins a point. Continue in this manner with one student serving as the scorekeeper.

Small Group/Whole Class ● ●/● ● ●

Get students out of their seats for this Think Quick! game. You will need a set of game cards, a bag, and a soft ball. Reproduce the Think Quick! Cards on card stock or other heavy paper. Cut the cards apart, and place them in a bag. Give the ball to the first student. Draw a card and read it aloud. The student holding the ball quickly tosses the ball to another person in the circle. That person must complete the sentence. Then, read aloud a new card. The student with the ball quickly tosses it to another student. The game continues in this manner until all students have had a turn.

Challenge students to come up with two or three Think Quick! Cards to add to the game.

The soapy water on the floor lead to...

One result of the tornado was...

Since she loved to run, Bella decided to...

The drummer wore headphones, due to the fact that...

Aiden prefers chocolate ice cream. Therefore, he...

Because he exercises daily, Jackson...

White, sticky frosting covered my fingers, so...

Because she had been late,...

If I eat too much candy...

Because of our flat tire, we...

Parts of South America are on the equator. Therefore,...

Many trees lose their leaves in autumn. The reason is that...

Grandmother watered the garden every day so that...

Always dispose of paper in a recycling bin because...

Cho spilled juice all over the white couch. As a result,...

The playground ball was wedged in the tree, so we...

It is important to tell your parents where you are because...

The other team was ahead, so we...

If I don't get my homework done...

Because of his bad cold, Adam...

Made in the USA
Middletown, DE
06 April 2022